NEW WAY

Gaston the giant
and other stories

Nelson

Gaston the giant

On a mountain high above the village,
lived Gaston the Giant.
Like all giants, Gaston ate a lot.
But unlike other giants,
Gaston wept when he was hungry.
Gaston was always hungry
so he was always weeping.

The people in the village thought
that the giants were very fierce.
When a giant appeared in the village,
they would drop their sacks of food and
run screaming from the kitchen,
so the giants could help themselves.

"Gaston can't come to the village,"
said the other giants.
"He will drown all the people."
"We must stop Gaston weeping,"
said one giant.
"Well, we could all take it in turns
to feed him," said another.
"Then he won't be hungry and
he won't cry," they all said.

So they all took turns to feed Gaston.
Gaston grew stronger and
stronger and the other giants grew
weaker and weaker.
So after one week the giants stopped.
Then Gaston grew hungry again and
he began to weep.

So they all tried to tell him
giant jokes to cheer him up.
It almost worked.
Gaston laughed and laughed
until he cried.
"Oh dear," said the giants.
"What can we do now?"

It had been a very hot summer that year.
No rain had fallen and
all the crops had died.
The villagers were hungry,
the giants were hungry and
Gaston was hungriest of all.

"We could eat the people in the village,"
said the giants.
"Let's go down and see if
they look good to eat."
So down the mountain went the giants
and Gaston went with them.
He was so hungry that
his tears formed a stream
                    and then a river
                            and then a lake.

The people watched and
were very happy.
"Gaston can save us,"
they said to the other giants.
"He can make our crops grow and
then there will be food for all.
If Gaston waters our fields,
we will share all our food with you."
So thanks to Gaston,
they all lived happily ever after.

The cat, the mouse and the magician

"Come in, little mouse," said the magician.

"How can I help you?"

"It's my squeak," squeaked the mouse.

"What's that?" said the magician. "Speak up."

"I can't," said the mouse.

"My squeak is so quiet that

the other mice laugh at me.

Please can you help me?"

"I'll try," said the magician.
So he made a spell.
"Abra-ca-da-bra," he said and
the mouse began to swell.
But when the mouse tried to squeak,
he roared, just like a lion.
"That's much too loud for a mouse,"
said the magician.
"The spell must be wrong."

Just then, the door opened and
a cat slid in.
"Good afternoon," he said.
"I'm having trouble with my eyes.
They shine too much in the dark.
All the mice see me coming,
so I can't catch them.
Please can you help me?"

Then the cat saw the mouse.
His fur stood on end.
He hissed and spat and
the mouse squeaked loudly
or rather, he roared like a lion.
Everything shook. The room shook,
the magician shook and
most of all the cat shook.
"Sorry," said the cat.
"I see now it's a lion-mouse."

"Now for your spell," said the magician.
This time the spell nearly worked.
The cat's eyes stopped shining.
But oh dear, what was that light
moving from side to side?
"My tail," said the cat. "It feels funny.
My tail is shining.
Now everyone will chase **me**," he cried.

"You two must stay here,"
said the magician.
"I must find out why my spells are wrong."
So the cat and the mouse lived
with the magician for three weeks.
They became great friends.

Then one day the cat said,
"I know why your spells are wrong.
It's your spelling.
Turn the spells round so that
you get your spelling right."
So the magician turned his spells round
and Hey Presto. It worked.
The cat's tail stopped shining and
the mouse stopped roaring.
So after that, they lived with
the magician and helped him
get his spelling right.

The magic porridge pot

There was an old woman who lived
in a house in a wood.
She lived with her naughty little boy.
The old woman had a magic porridge pot.
Every day she went into the kitchen
to make porridge for breakfast.

She put the big old pot on the stove and
she said, "Start pot, start."
Then she sat down by the stove
and watched the pot.
When the pot was full, the old woman said,
"Stop pot, stop."
Then the old woman and her little boy
sat down at the table to eat the porridge.

One day the old woman went out.
She left the naughty little boy
asleep at home, safe in his little bed.
She walked to the other side of the wood
and went into a field to pick mushrooms.

When the naughty little boy woke up,
he went downstairs.
He said to himself,
"I will make the porridge today."
So he took the big old pot and
put it on the stove.

"Start pot, start,"
said the naughty little boy.
Then he sat down by the stove
and watched the pot.
When the pot was full,
the naughty little boy said,
"Pot, stop."

But the pot did not stop.

It went on cooking and cooking.

The porridge ran over the top of the pot.

It ran down the side of the pot.

It ran down the stove and on to the floor.

The naughty little boy said,

"Pot, stop. Pot, **stop**."

But still the pot did not stop.
The porridge ran across the floor and
under the door.
It ran down the path to the gate.
Just then the old woman came home.
She saw all the porridge.

She ran into the kitchen and saw
the big old pot on the stove.
"Stop pot, stop," she said.
The pot stopped cooking and
it stopped making porridge.
And from that day on, the big old pot
only made porridge when
the old woman asked it.